Table of Contents

W9-BPJ-479

continued

Section 2

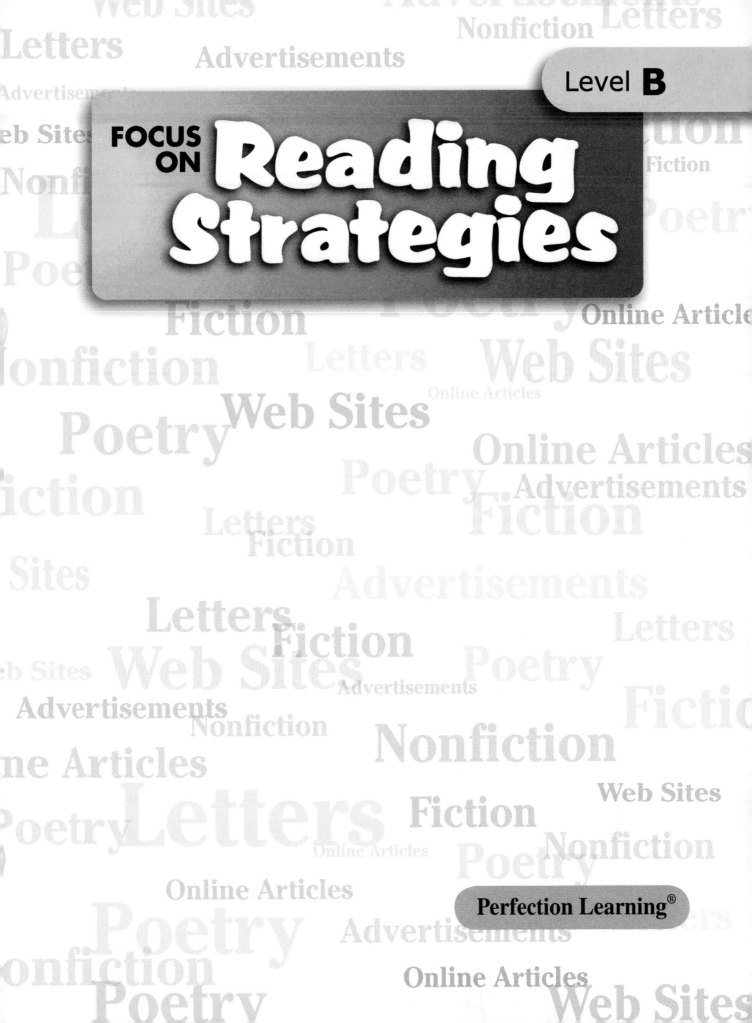

Editorial Director: Susan C. Thies
Editor: Kathryn Winzenburg
Design Director: Randy Messer
Cover Design: Michael A. Aspengren
Book Design: Deborah Lea Bell
Contributing Designers: Michael A. Aspengren, Tobi Cunningham, Michelle Glass, Emily Greazel

Reviewers:

Kathryn Black
Language Program Specialist
Mesa Public Schools
Mesa, Arizona

Cindy Brunswick
Literacy Coordinator
Center for School Improvement
University of Chicago
Chicago, Illinois

L. Michelle Johnson, M.Ed.
Education Department
Washington College
Chestertown, Maryland

Jan Keese
K–12 Reading Facilitator
Ankeny Community Schools
Ankeny, Iowa

Illustration Credits: Margaret Sanfillippo Lindmark p. 6 (inset illustration); ©perfectionlearning.com pp. 16, 17, 39, 42, 55, 56, 58, 59, 60, 61, 63, 73, 79, 82

Some images Corel Professional Photos; Dynamic Graphics Liquid Library; www.clipart.com; www.digitalstock.com; www.istockphotos.com; www.photos.com

For information, contact
Perfection Learning® Corporation
1000 North Second Avenue, P.O. Box 500
Logan, Iowa 51546-0500
Phone: 1-800-831-4190
Fax: 1-800-543-2745
perfectionlearning.com

ISBN 0-7891-6792-1

1 2 3 4 5 6 BA 11 10 09 08 07 06

Lesson 1

Snakes!
from Schoolhouse on the Prairie

• *Historical Fiction*

Heads Up You are going to read part of a story. Sometimes, pictures can give you clues about a story. They can give you clues about characters. They can also give you clues about what will happen in the story.

Look at this picture. It goes with the story you will be reading. What will happen in the story? Write your ideas on the lines.

_____

_____

_____

_____

_____

_____

_____

Good readers think while they read. One way of thinking while you read is to *ask yourself questions.* As you read "Snakes!" you will notice Think-Along Questions. Stop and answer these questions. Then read on. You may add questions of your own. Also, as you read, circle or highlight words you don't know.

Snakes!

from Schoolhouse on the Prairie
by Cynthia Mercati

1 May turned to June. The days got warmer.

2 One morning, I found a large bull snake coiled on my desk! I froze in my tracks. I clamped a hand over my mouth. I tried not to scream. But I hated snakes!

3 Laughter rang out. I turned around quickly. The older boys were watching me from the doorway.

4 Still laughing, the boys ran in all directions. I could tell they were proud of their trick.

Who do you think the person who uses "I" is?

5 They were probably a little scared too. What would I do to them? Would I tell their parents?

6 I decided not to make a fuss. But just looking at the snake made me shiver!

7 I grabbed the broom. I scooped up the snake with it.

8 It stirred and wriggled! I made a face. My heart started hammering. But I didn't scream!

9 I held the broom straight out in front of me. I stomped out the door. I marched through the schoolyard. The children followed. They giggled and pointed.

Why do the children giggle and point?

10   I flung the snake off the broom. It landed in the prairie grass. Then I walked back to the school.

11   "That was a mean thing the boys did," Grace said. "Are you going to make 'em sit on the dunce chair?"

12   "I don't use a dunce chair," I told Grace.

13   Some teachers used a dunce chair for punishment. They made **unruly** students sit on a chair in the corner of the room, facing the wall. On the chair, the teachers hung a sign that said "Dunce." *To be a dunce* meant "to be stupid."

How would you feel if you had to sit in the dunce chair?

14   I didn't believe in shaming children!

15   One of the younger boys asked, "Are you gonna beat 'em, Miss Witherspoon?"

16   I didn't believe in beatings, either!

17   "Of course not, Caleb," I said. "There was no harm done. Snakes are nothing to be afraid of."

Why does Miss Witherspoon say that snakes are nothing to be afraid of?

18   I went inside. I didn't have to pretend to be brave anymore. I sank down at my desk. My heart was still pounding.

19   I really hated snakes!

Make Sense of Words When you come to a word you don't know, you can try to understand the meaning by:

- using picture clues.

- rereading the sentence and using the *context clues*. These are the other words in the sentence and the paragraph.

- breaking the word into parts. Sometimes you will find one or more words you know within a word.

- using the dictionary or asking an adult.

1. Read the sentence from paragraph 13 of the story and answer the following questions.

> They made **unruly** students sit on a chair in the corner of the room, facing the wall.

a. Who are "they" in the sentence?

_____

_____

b. What was this chair called?

_____

c. Why did students have to sit in this chair?

_____

_____

d. Why do you think the chair faced the wall?

_____

_____

e. What do you think **unruly** means?

_____

_____

Now find out the meanings of the other words you didn't know.

Read with Understanding What can you tell about the story by looking at the picture on page 6?

Ⓐ The teacher has 10 children in her class.

Ⓑ The children think the snake trick is funny.

Ⓒ The story takes place in Iowa.

Ⓓ The teacher is 20 years old.

Understand by Seeing It You learn about Miss Witherspoon in "Snakes!" You learn about her from what she does. You also learn about her from what she says to others. You even learn about her from what she thinks. In the character web below, fill in words that describe Miss Witherspoon.

Miss Witherspoon

Write to Learn   Choose one of the children from the picture on page 6. Using picture clues, describe what you think the child is like. Tell about his or her family and friends. Tell what kind of person he or she is.

Lesson 2

Cardboard Yo-Yo

from **Tops (and Other Spinning Toys)**

• *Directions*

Heads Up Pictures can help when you are reading directions. They can show the materials you need. They can also show the steps you need to follow.

The name of this passage is "Cardboard Yo-Yo." What do you think a cardboard yo-yo is? What do you think it looks like? What makes it different from a regular yo-yo? Draw a picture of a cardboard yo-yo in the box. Then tell about what you drew on the lines on the next page.

Good readers think while they read. One way of thinking while you read is to *ask yourself questions*. As you read "Cardboard Yo-Yo," you will notice Think-Along Questions. Stop and answer these questions. Then read on. You may add questions of your own. Also, as you read, circle or highlight words you don't know.

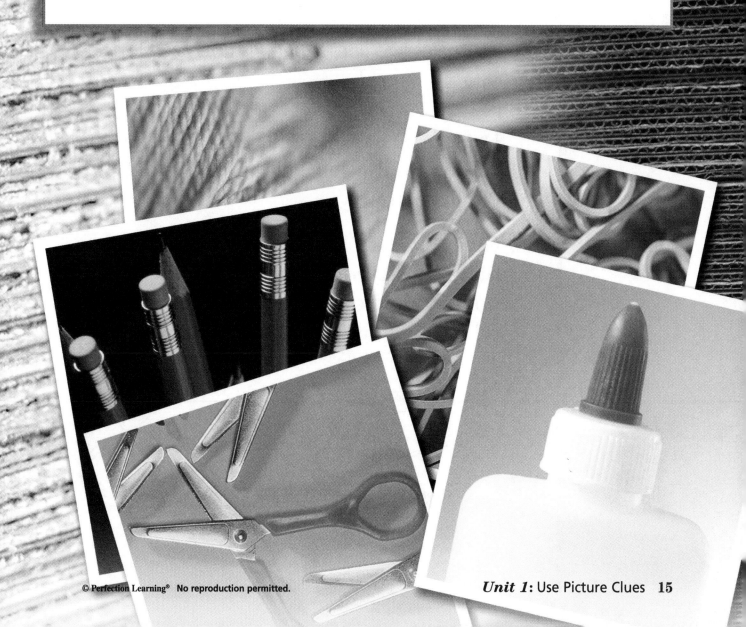

Cardboard Yo-Yo
from Tops (and Other Spinning Toys)
by Beth Dvergsten Stevens

Needs
clean cardboard from
   a pizza box
1-pound coffee can
scissors
glue
3" pencil
string
small rubber bands

How do you think the coffee can will be used?

Steps

1. Draw around a 1-pound coffee can on the cardboard. Do this six times. Cut out the circles carefully.

2. Glue three circles together to make one **disk**. Only glue around the outer edges. Try not to glue the center. Do the same with the other three circles.

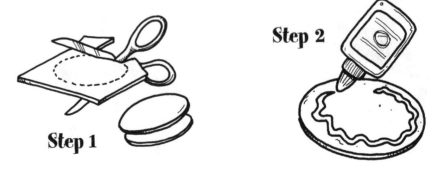

Step 1   Step 2

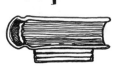

3. Set the disks under a heavy book for five minutes.

> What else would work if you didn't have a heavy book?

4. Mark the centers of the disks. Set them on top of a large piece of cardboard. Push a pencil tip through the center of each disk to create holes.

5. Push the pencil tip through the hole in one disk. Move the disk toward the eraser end.

Steps 4 & 5

6. Cut a piece of string about 45" long. Tie one end around the pencil.

> What would happen if the string were too long or too short?

7. Push the pencil tip through the hole in the other disk. The disks should be about ½" apart. Center them on the pencil. The string will be between the disks.

Steps 6 & 7

8. Wind rubber bands around the pencil ends to hold the disks in place.

9. Wind up the string and try out your yo-yo.

Make Sense of Words When you come to a word you don't know, you can try to understand the meaning by:

- using picture clues.

- rereading the sentence and using the *context clues*. These are the other words in the sentence and the paragraph.

- breaking the word into parts. Sometimes you will find one or more words you know within a word.

- using the dictionary or asking an adult.

1. a. Find the word **disk** in Step 2. Predict what the word means. Write it on the lines below.

_____

_____

   b. Look at the pictures with the directions. What shape is being cut from the cardboard and glued together?

_____

_____

   c. Now what do you think the word **disk** means?

_____

_____

Now find out the meanings of the other words you didn't know. Don't forget to use the picture clues.

Read with Understanding Which of the following steps does not have a picture to go with it?

Ⓐ Cut out the circles carefully.

Ⓑ Wind up the string and try out your yo-yo.

Ⓒ Only glue around the outer edges.

Ⓓ Set the disks under a heavy book for five minutes.

Understand by Seeing It Directions always have two kinds of words—*verbs* and *nouns*. Verbs are action words. They tell what you do. Nouns are persons, places, things, and ideas. In directions, nouns are mostly things.

The words in the box are from the directions for "Cardboard Yo-Yo." Some are verbs. Some are nouns. Write each word in the correct column in the chart.

draw	cardboard	circles	set	pizza	book
use	scissors	pencil	push	create	cut

Nouns	Verbs

Draw a picture for Step 1 of the directions.

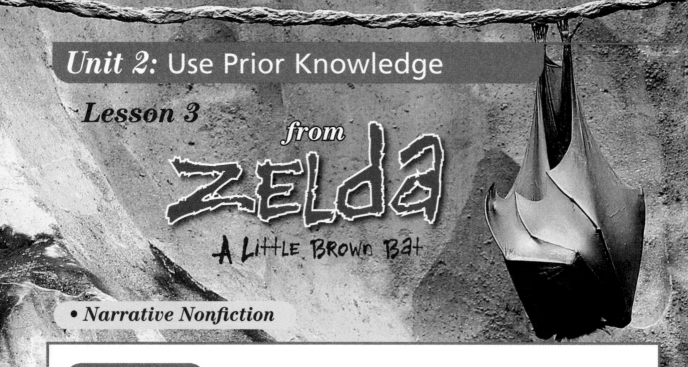

Lesson 3

from ZELDA
A Little Brown Bat

• *Narrative Nonfiction*

Heads Up You are about to read a nonfiction story about a brown bat. Think about what you know about bats. What you already know is called **prior knowledge**. What questions would you like to ask about bats?

Use this KWL chart. Fill out the **K** part with what you already know. Fill out the **W** part with questions you have. You will fill out the **L** column after you read the story.

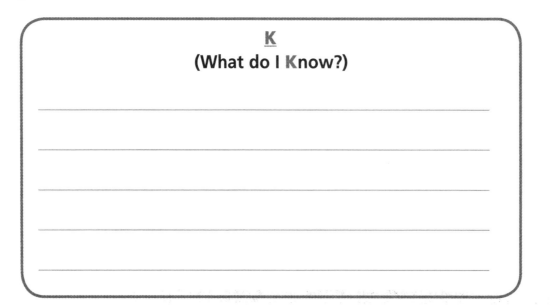

K
(What do I Know?)

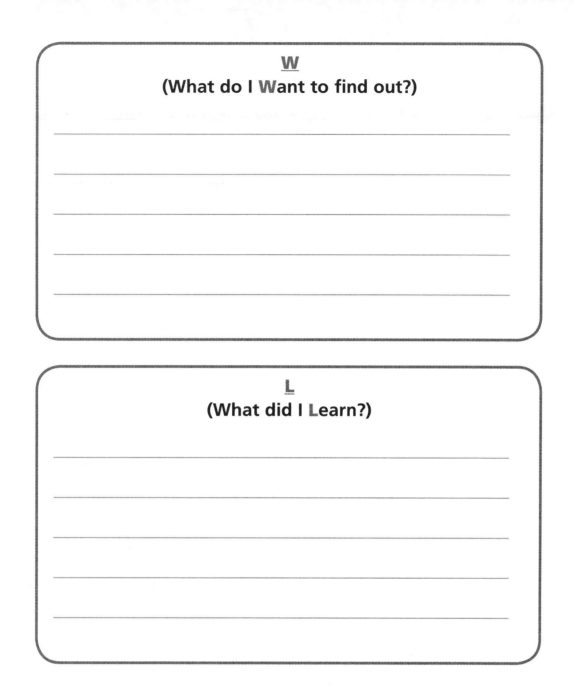

W
(What do I Want to find out?)

L
(What did I Learn?)

Good readers think while they read. One way of thinking while you read is to *ask yourself questions*. As you read *Zelda: A Little Brown Bat*, you will notice Think-Along Questions. Stop and answer these questions. Then read on. You may add questions of your own. Also, as you read, circle or highlight words you don't know.

from Zelda: A Little Brown Bat

by Bonnie Highsmith Taylor

1   Zelda opened her eyes. She looked around. She was hanging upside down. So were the other bats in the roosting place.

2   It was almost dusk. It was time to wake up. The bats began to stir. The time had come to fly outside and look for food.

3   Zelda was a little brown bat. She was about three and a half inches long. She weighed less than an ounce.

What is something else that would be about this size?

4   Little brown bats are found in most states. Texas, Florida, and California are the only states where they don't live.

5   Bats roost and hibernate in a lot of different places. They are found in caves, mines, hollow trees, and buildings.

6   Zelda's roost was in the attic of an old vacant house. It was where she had been born. About 40 females lived in the *colony*, or group.

If you were a bat, where would you want to roost?

7   Male bats and younger females were in another roosting place. That group was called a *bachelor colony*.

8   Zelda would give birth in a few weeks. It would be Zelda's first time to be a mother. She would have only one baby. It would be called a *pup*.

9   Bats live a long time. The average life span is 10 to 12 years. Some bats have been known to live over 20 years.

10   Zelda and the other bats left the roost. They flew into the night. First, they flew to a nearby stream.

11   Zelda zoomed low. She lowered her bottom jaw. Then she scooped up water. Now she was ready to start feeding.

12   The air was alive with **mosquitoes** and other insects. Zelda ate almost half her weight in insects. One little brown bat can eat 500 insects in an hour.

13   Zelda stopped to rest several times. By early morning, she was full and tired.

14   Zelda flew back to her roosting place. She was covered with dust. She cleaned herself very carefully. Then she hung by her claws and went to sleep.

Why do you think bats hang upside down to sleep?

Make Sense of Words   When you come to a word you don't know, you can try to understand the meaning by:

- using picture clues.

- rereading the sentence and using the *context clues.* These are the other words in the sentence and the paragraph.

- breaking the word into parts. Sometimes you will find one or more words you know within a word.

- using the dictionary or asking an adult.

1. a. Find the word **mosquitoes** in paragraph 12. Look it up in a dictionary. Remember, plural forms of words are not in the dictionary. Instead, look up *mosquito*. Write the meaning on the lines below.

   _____

   _____

   b. Draw a picture of a mosquito in the box below.

   ```
   ┌─────────────────────────────────────┐
   │                                     │
   │                                     │
   │                                     │
   │                                     │
   │                                     │
   └─────────────────────────────────────┘
   ```

Now find out the meanings of the other words you didn't know.

Now add to the **L** part of the KWL chart in the Heads Up section. Write three things you learned about bats.

Which prior knowledge would be useful when reading this story?

Ⓐ Which animals owls hunt at night

Ⓑ How humans digest food

Ⓒ Dracula could turn into a bat.

Ⓓ Bats sleep during the day and hunt at night.

Understand by Seeing It Fill in the web below with facts about bats. Use your prior knowledge. Also use what you learned from the story.

BATS

Write to Learn   Write a letter to a friend. Tell what you already knew about bats. Then share what you learned about bats from the story. Include the fact you thought was most interesting.

Dear _____,

_____

_____

_____

_____

_____

_____

_____

_____

        Sincerely, _____

Lesson 4

Nelson: George Washington's Horse

from Presidential Pet Tails

• *Narrative Nonfiction*

Heads Up This story is about a former president's favorite pet. Use prior knowledge to make connections with the story. Do you have a favorite pet? On the lines below and on the next page, write about it. What kind of pet is it? What is it like? Do you still have it? How long have you had it? Why is it your favorite? If you don't have a favorite pet, tell what kind of pet you would like to have.

_____

_____

_____

_____

Good readers think while they read. One way of thinking while you read is to *ask yourself questions*. As you read "Nelson: George Washington's Horse," you will notice Think-Along Questions. Stop and answer these questions. Then read on. You may add questions of your own. Also, as you read, circle or highlight words you don't know.

Nelson: George Washington's Horse
from Presidential Pet Tails
by Kathleen M. Muldoon

1 George Washington was our first president. He also owned the first presidential pets. But George Washington did not live in the White House. It had not yet been built when he became president in 1789.

What else do you know about George Washington?

2 President Washington, his family, and his pets lived in two different houses. The first was in New York City.

3 New York City was then the nation's capital. Later, the capital moved to Philadelphia. So did the president.

4 Even before becoming president, George Washington loved animals. He grew up on a farm in Virginia. He especially liked dogs and horses. They helped him when he went hunting.

5 As an adult, Washington had a farm. It was called Mount Vernon. There he kept many animals. Washington had 130 horses.

6 Washington was an excellent rider. He rode horses into battle. He loved them all. But he had two favorites. He rode both horses during the Revolutionary War.

What was the Revolutionary War?

7 The first was named Blueskin. His hair was the color of gray stone. Washington liked him

because he ran fast. He never seemed to get tired. Running was very important for an army horse.

8   But the other horse became George Washington's pet. His name was Nelson. General Washington rode Nelson into the important battle at Yorktown.

9   When Washington became president, he kept Nelson and Blueskin. Their work in war was done. They were free to spend their days grazing in a pasture.

10   Nelson's skin shone like a chestnut. He was **tamer** than most horses. Sometimes President Washington went to the pasture fence and called, "Nelson!"

11   Nelson would stop grazing. He would run to the president. Then he would rub his head on Washington's arm.

12   Washington treated his horses like family members. He cared about them very deeply.

Why do you think George Washington loved horses so much?

13   Blueskin and Nelson lived for many years. In 1797, Washington's term as president ended. He moved his family and animals back to Mount Vernon.

14   Nelson remained his special pet. George Washington continued riding horses until he died two years later.

Make Sense of Words When you come to a word you don't know, you can try to understand the meaning by:

- using picture clues.

- rereading the sentence and using the *context clues*. These are the other words in the sentence and the paragraph.

- breaking the word into parts. Sometimes you will find one or more words you know within a word.

- using the dictionary or asking an adult.

Reread this sentence from paragraph 10.

> He was **tamer** than most horses.

This sentence is telling about Nelson. If you are not sure what **tamer** means, just read the next four sentences.

> Sometimes President Washington went to the pasture fence and called, "Nelson!"
> Nelson would stop grazing. He would run to the president. Then he would rub his head on Washington's arm.

1. You should now have an idea of what **tamer** or **tame** means. Put an X in front of the sentences below that describe something that is **tame**.

❏ My bird puts her head down so I can scratch the back of her neck.

❏ The squirrel runs away when people come near.

❏ The farm cat hisses at the children.

❏ The circus lion lets a man put his head in its mouth.

❏ The monkey shakes hands with the people at the zoo.

Read with Understanding You have read about George Washington's favorite pet. You could use the facts you read as prior knowledge later. With which story could you use these facts?

Ⓐ A story about Abraham Lincoln's childhood

Ⓑ A story about George Washington's life

Ⓒ A story about how zoos are created

Ⓓ A story about a crazy parrot named Pedro

Understand by Seeing It Think about the facts you learned from this story. They could be used as prior knowledge later. Record facts you learned in the boxes below.

Fact #1
_____

Fact #2
_____

Fact #3
_____

Fact #4
_____

Write to Learn Review the facts you learned about George Washington and his favorite pet. Then write a scene that could have happened between Washington and one of his pets. Use your prior knowledge.

Lesson 5

THE HAT

from **Days with Frog and Toad**

• *Short Story*

Heads Up When you sequence events, you put them in the order they happened. You do this when you retell a story. It is important to keep the events in order. If you don't, the story won't make sense.

This story is about what happens on Toad's birthday. Think about your last birthday. What did you do? Write what you did on the next page. Sequence the events, or put them in the correct order.

Good readers think while they read. One way of thinking while you read is to *ask yourself questions*. As you read "The Hat," you will notice Think-Along Questions. Stop and answer these questions. Then read on. You may add questions of your own. Also, as you read, circle or highlight words you don't know.

THE HAT

from Days with Frog and Toad
by Arnold Lobel

1   On Toad's birthday Frog gave him a hat. Toad was delighted.

2   "Happy birthday," said Frog.

3   Toad put on the hat. It fell down over his eyes.

4   "I am sorry," said Frog. "That hat is much too big for you. I will give you something else."

5   "No," said Toad. "This hat is your present to me. I like it. I will wear it the way it is."

What do you think will happen next?

6   Frog and Toad went for a walk. Toad tripped over a rock. He bumped into a tree. He fell in a hole.

7   "Frog," said Toad, "I can't see anything. I will not be able to wear your beautiful present. This is a sad birthday for me."

8   Frog and Toad were sad for a while. Then Frog said, "Toad, here is what you must do. Tonight when you go to bed you must think some very **big** thoughts. Those big thoughts will make your head grow larger. In the morning your new hat may fit."

9   "What a good idea," said Toad.

10   That night when Toad went to bed he thought the biggest thoughts that he could think. Toad thought about giant sunflowers. He thought

about tall oak trees. He thought about high mountains covered with snow. Then Toad fell asleep.

What are some other "big thoughts"?

11   Frog came into Toad's house. He came in quietly. Frog found the hat and took it to his house.

12   Frog poured some water on the hat. He put the hat in a warm place to dry. It began to shrink. That hat grew smaller and smaller.

13   Frog went back to Toad's house. Toad was still fast asleep. Frog put the hat back on the hook where he found it.

Why do you think Frog does this?

14   When Toad woke up in the morning, he put the hat on his head. It was just the right size.

15   Toad ran to Frog's house. "Frog, Frog!" he cried. "All those big thoughts have made my head much larger. Now I can wear your present!"

16   Frog and Toad went for a walk. Toad did not trip over a rock. He did not bump into a tree. He did not fall in a hole.

17   It turned out to be a very pleasant day after Toad's birthday.

Have you ever gotten a present that didn't fit or work for you? What did you do?

My Thoughts

Make Sense of Words   When you come to a word you don't know, you can try to understand the meaning by:

- using picture clues.

- rereading the sentence and using the *context clues*. These are the other words in the sentence and the paragraph.

- breaking the word into parts. Sometimes you will find one or more words you know within a word.

- using the dictionary or asking an adult.

1. A *synonym* is a word that has the same or nearly the same meaning as another word. In this story, Frog tells Toad to go to bed and think **big** thoughts. The author uses three synonyms for **big**. Find them and record them below.

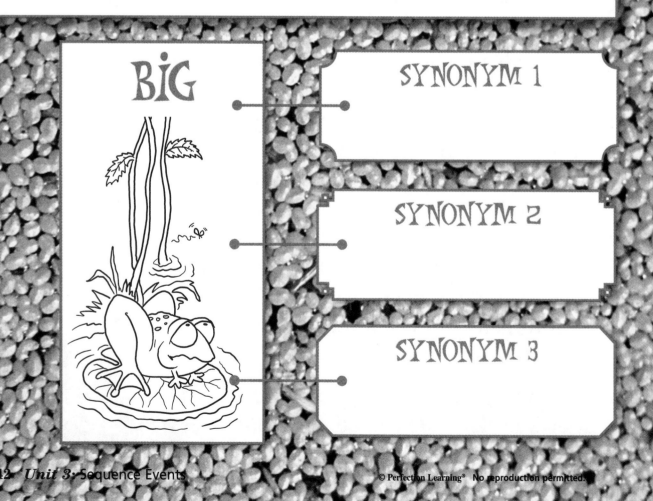

BIG

SYNONYM 1

SYNONYM 2

SYNONYM 3

Read with Understanding Which of the following events in the story happened *first*?

Ⓐ Frog poured water on the hat.

Ⓑ Toad thought the biggest thoughts he could think.

Ⓒ Toad bumped into a tree.

Ⓓ Frog gave Toad a hat for his birthday.

Understand by Seeing It Read through the events below. Then fill in the chart by writing each event in the correct order.

The hat fell down over Toad's eyes.
Toad did not fall in a hole.
The hat began to shrink.
"Now I can wear your present!" Toad cried.
Frog told Toad to think very big thoughts.

1.

2.

3.

4.

5.

What do you think happened the day after Toad's birthday? Begin with the morning. Tell what happened with Toad's hat. Then make up what happened the rest of the day. Tell the story in sequence.

_____

_____

_____

_____

_____

_____

_____

_____

_____

_____

_____

Busy, Buzzy Bee

• *Narrative Nonfiction*

Heads Up In science, the order in which things happen is important. When you read, you must pay close attention to the sequence of events.

What do you think a day in the life of a bee is like? Fill in the sequence chart on the next page. Then read the story to see how much you know about bees.

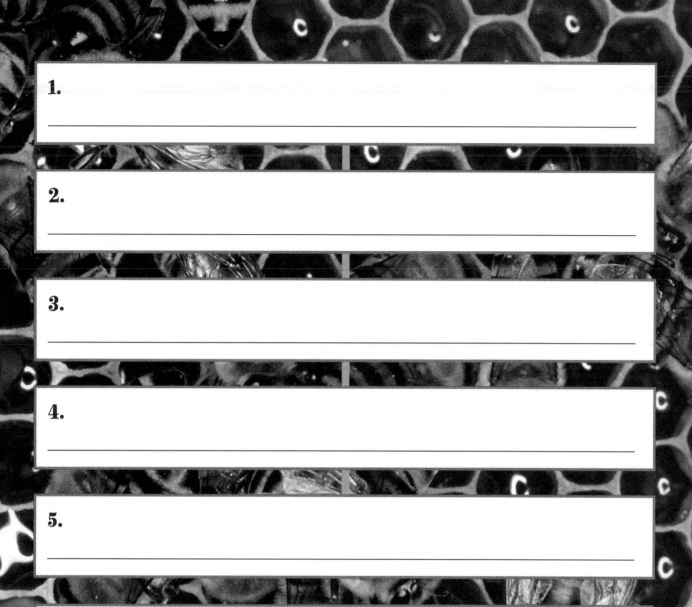

1. _____
_____

2. _____
_____

3. _____
_____

4. _____
_____

5. _____
_____

Good readers think while they read. One way of thinking while you read is to *ask yourself questions*. As you read *Busy, Buzzy Bee* you will notice Think-Along Questions. Stop and answer these questions. Then read on. You may add questions of your own. Also, as you read, circle or highlight words you don't know.

Busy, Buzzy Bee

by Karen Wallace

1   Busy Bee has work to do. She crawls out of her hive.

2   She spreads her wings. Busy Bee is looking for a flower.

Why is she looking for a flower?

3   Busy Bee flies over a stream. She flies past an oak tree and into a field. The field is full of wild flowers.

4   Busy Bee lands on a flower. Each flower holds sweet drops of nectar. Bees make nectar into honey. Nectar and honey are food for bees.

5   Busy Bee laps up the nectar with her long, narrow tongue. She will take it back to the hive.

6   Each flower holds grains of pollen. Flower pollen is good for bees too.

7   The pollen sticks to Busy Bee's furry body. She brings it to the hive on her two back legs.

8   Busy Bee is a worker bee. Inside the hive, there are thousands like her. All worker bees are female.

9   Busy Bee dances a dance. She waggles her bottom. She crawls in circles. Her dance shows the other workers the way to find the flower nectar.

Why do you think bees show the way with a dance? What else could they do?

10   Inside the hive, the bees make cells. Some are for the honey the bees make from nectar. Some are for the pollen the bees have collected. Some are for the eggs that the queen bee lays.

11   Busy Bee has work to do. First she feeds the drone bees.

12   All drone bees are male. The drones mate with a queen bee.

13   Then Busy Bee feeds the queen bee. The queen bee lays a thousand eggs every day.

14   Inside their cells, the eggs hatch into bee grubs. Busy Bee and thousands like her take some pollen mixed with honey. They feed it to the hungry grubs.

15   Busy Bee has work to do. She feeds the bee grubs every day. When the grubs are nine days old she seals their cells with waxy covers.

16   Inside their cells, the bee grubs change. They grow legs and wings. They grow long, narrow tongues.

17   In twelve days they change from grubs to bees. They crawl out and wait for their new wings to dry.

My Thoughts

GO ON

My Thoughts

18   Busy Bee and thousands like her touch the young bees with their feelers. They make them welcome in the hive. They feed them honey from the cells.

How do humans make babies feel welcome?

19   Busy Bee has work to do. The young bees are hungry. Where can she find more flower nectar? Where can she find more flower pollen?

20   Look! Another bee is dancing! She's found a garden full of flowers.

21   She waggles her bottom. She crawls in circles. Her dance shows Busy Bee how to find the garden.

What will Busy Bee do next?

22   Busy Bee and thousands like her fly from the hive. They find the garden full of flowers. They drink the nectar. They take the pollen. Busy Bee has work to do.

1. The word web below is about bees. Choose words from the list that have special meanings related to bees. Write each word in one of the web circles.

Word Bank

cells	feelers	hive	crawl	hungry
grubs	pollen	nectar	grow	thousands

Bees

Sequence the events below. They describe the life cycle of a bee.

_____ The bee grubs' cells are sealed with waxy covers.

_____ The queen bee lays a thousand eggs.

_____ The bees crawl out of the cells and wait for their wings to dry.

_____ The eggs hatch into bee grubs.

In the boxes below, draw what happens when a bee leaves a hive to find a flower. Make sure to draw the events in the right sequence.

1

2

3

4

Write to Learn Pretend you are a scientist. You are studying bees. In your field journal, record what you see bees doing today. Make sure to sequence the events.

from DINOSAURS

• *Narrative Nonfiction*

Heads Up   This is from a book about different kinds of dinosaurs.

What do you know about dinosaurs? Record facts you know about dinosaurs on the lines on the next page. What are different kinds of dinosaurs? What did they eat? How did they look? When did they live?

Dinosaur Facts

As you read, use what you learned in the lessons. Look at the pictures to get more meaning. Think about what you already know about dinosaurs. Pay attention to the sequence of events. Answer the Think-Along Questions as you read.

from DINOSAURS
by Norman Bilbrough

Meat-eating dinosaurs were called *carnivores*. Tyrannosaurus was one of the biggest carnivores. It was taller than a bus.

Tyrannosaurus killed animals with its clawed feet. It also ate dinosaurs that were already dead. Its teeth were longer than your fingers. When its teeth wore out, new ones grew.

Carnivores had big brains. Carnivores needed bigger brains than the plant-eating dinosaurs.

Why does a carnivore need a big brain?

Tyrannosaurus stalked and ate the huge triceratops. Tyrannosaurus had a brain the size of a grapefruit. Triceratops had a brain the size of a walnut.

GO ON

Review 1 57

Dinosaurs *continued*

The little troodon had a big brain. It could run fast. It ran past nests and snatched baby dinosaurs to eat. Troodon hunted in the dark.

Why did Troodon hunt in the dark?

Plant-eating dinosaurs were called *herbivores*. Brachiosaurus ate leaves from the tops of trees like a giraffe.

It ate the weight of two cars a day. It did not chew its food. It swallowed its food whole.

Brachiosaurus had stones in its stomach to grind its food up. These stones were called *gastroliths*. Brachiosaurus spat out the stones when they were smooth. Then it swallowed new ones.

Herbivores had to defend themselves against carnivores. Many lived in herds for safety.

Euoplocephalus had armor plating and horns all over its body. It had a club on the end of its tail. A blow from this club could kill a tyrannosaurus.

Kentrosaurus had plates on its neck and back and sharp spikes on its tail

Centrosaurus had a head shield.

Dinosaurs' feet were like birds' feet. Their bones were hollow like birds' bones. Some dinosaurs had birdlike scales.

Birds came from dinosaurs. Scientists now think that the first bird, called *archaeopteryx*, was really a dinosaur.

Dinosaurs left tracks all over the world. Their footprints were filled with sand, and some turned into rocks. These are called *trackaways*.

Have you ever seen animal tracks? What kinds?

Dinosaurs lived on Earth for 150 million years. There were 64 million years between the last dinosaur and the first human. Humans have lived on Earth for 1 million years.

Scientists think that a comet hit Earth 65 million years ago. It caused huge fires. Dust clouds covered the sun. Earth became very cold.

After the comet hit the Earth, lizards and frogs still caught insects. Fish still swam in the sea. Crocodiles still lived on land and water. But all the dinosaurs died.

1. Which statement is true based on the pictures?

   Ⓐ Humans wouldn't even reach a Tyrannosaurus's knee.

   Ⓑ Humans are about the same size as the Tyrannosaurus was.

   Ⓒ Humans would reach a Tyrannosaurus's shoulder.

   Ⓓ The Tyrannosaurus was smaller than humans are.

2. Which piece of prior knowledge would have helped you understand this story?

   Ⓐ Some lizards are related to dinosaurs.

   Ⓑ The Tyrannosaurus was fierce.

   Ⓒ Carnivores are meat-eaters and herbivores are plant-eaters.

   Ⓓ Dinosaurs are studied in museums.

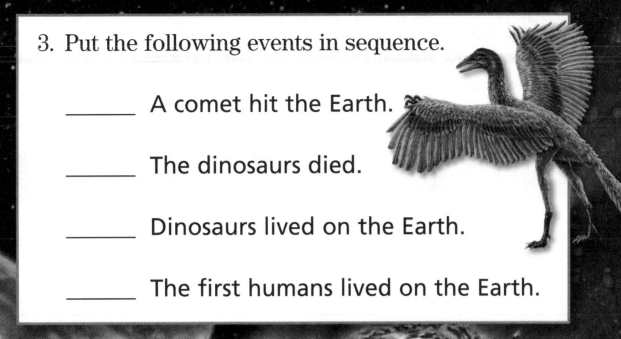

3. Put the following events in sequence.

_____ A comet hit the Earth.

_____ The dinosaurs died.

_____ Dinosaurs lived on the Earth.

_____ The first humans lived on the Earth.

Understand by Seeing It You already had some prior knowledge about dinosaurs. You probably learned some new facts too. What did you learn? Fill in the chart below.

WHAT I KNEW

_____

_____

_____

_____

WHAT I LEARNED

_____

_____

_____

_____

Write to Learn   Imagine you are a scientist who studies dinosaurs. Write in your journal. Tell about what you study to learn more about how dinosaurs lived millions of years ago.

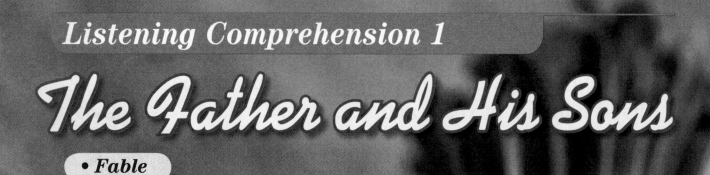

The Father and His Sons

- **Fable**

Listening comprehension is a valuable skill. Learning and practicing good listening skills will be helpful to you in your life inside and outside of school. When you listen, it is important to focus your attention on the speaker.

Listen as your teacher reads the fable "The Father and His Sons." Then answer the questions below.

1. How many sons does the father have?

   _____

2. What happened when the father separated the bundle of sticks?

   _____

   _____

3. What lesson was the father trying to teach his sons with the sticks?

   _____

   _____

   _____

Lesson 7

from

I Saw You in the Bathtub
and Other Folk Rhymes

- *Folk Rhyme*

Heads Up You can predict what will happen in a story. Predicting means making a good guess based on some facts. Knowing the subject of a story can help you predict.

This rhyme is about a child and a skunk. What do you predict will happen? Why? Write your prediction on the lines.

_____

_____

_____

_____

_____

_____

Good readers think while they read. One way of thinking while you read is to *ask yourself questions*. As you read this folk rhyme, you will notice Think-Along Questions. Stop and answer these questions. Then read on. You may add questions of your own. Also, as you read, circle or highlight words you don't know.

My Thoughts

from **I Saw You in the Bathtub and Other Folk Rhymes**
by Alvin Schwartz

Oh, I stuck my head
In a little **skunk's** hole,
And the little skunk said,
"Well, bless my soul.

> What does "bless my soul" mean?

Take it out!
Take it out!
Take it out!
Remove it!"
When I did not take it out,

> Why do you think the child does not take his or her head out?

The little skunk said,
"You had better take it out,
Or you'll wish you were dead.

> What is the skunk talking about when it says, "you'll wish you were dead"?

Take it out!
Take it out!
Take it out!
Remove it!"

I removed it . . .

Sssssssssssssssssssssssssss.

TOO LATE!

> What happened?

Make Sense of Words   When you come to a word you don't know, you can try to understand the meaning by:

- using picture clues.

- rereading the sentence and using the *context clues*. These are the other words in the sentence and the paragraph.

- breaking the word into parts. Sometimes you will find one or more words you know within a word.

- using the dictionary or asking an adult.

You can learn more about words by looking them up in the dictionary. You probably know what a **skunk** is. You can learn more about a **skunk** by looking up the word in the dictionary. Look up the word. Then fill in the questions below.

skunk

1. a. On which page did you find the word? _____

    b. What are the guide words found at the top of the page?

    _____

    c. What more did you learn about a skunk from the dictionary entry?

    _____

    _____

Read with Understanding What do you predict will happen next in the story?

Ⓐ The child will take a bath.

Ⓑ The child will hug the skunk.

Ⓒ The child will stick his or her head back inside the hole.

Ⓓ The child will look for another hole.

Understand by Seeing It Look back at your prediction from Heads Up. Were you right?

To find out if a prediction is right, you look at the events in a story.

Think about the three main events in the folk rhyme. Draw each one in the correct box. Then write what happened.

Event 1

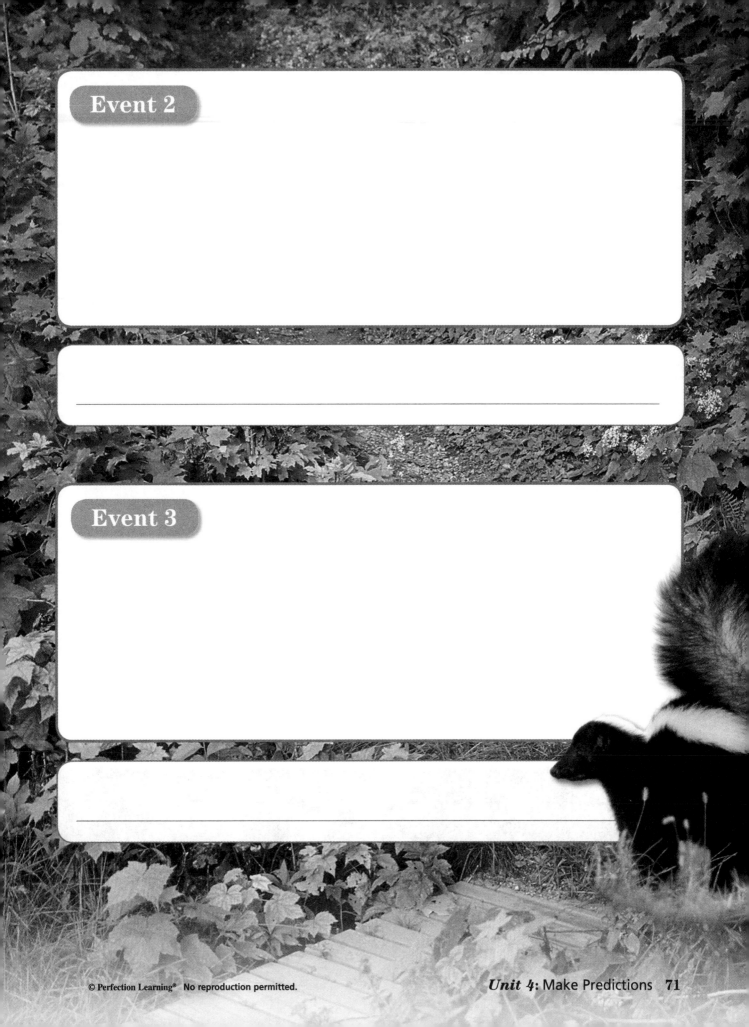

Event 2

Event 3

Write to Learn Continue the folk rhyme. Use your prediction of what will happen next.

_____

_____

_____

_____

_____

_____

_____

_____

_____

_____

Lesson 8

from

Heroes of Beesville

• *Chapter Book Excerpt*

Heads Up This story is about four animal friends who are having trouble cooperating on a school project. In the story, their teacher gives them a magic whistle. The whistle takes the friends on different adventures where they meet other animals to help them. The friends can only return home after they understand what the animals are teaching them. On this adventure, the friends meet an animal that can teach them about cooperation.

Predict what animal helps the four friends learn about cooperation. Then explain why this animal would be a good teacher about cooperation. Write in the spaces below. Then read the story to see if you were right.

_____

_____

_____

_____

_____

_____

Good readers think while they read. One way of thinking while you read is to *ask yourself questions*. As you read this story, you will notice Think-Along Questions. Stop and answer these questions. Then read on. You may add questions of your own. Also, as you read, circle or highlight words you don't know.

from *Heroes of Beesville*
by Coach John Wooden
(with Steve Jamison and Bonnie Graves)

My Thoughts

1   "Miles," Inch said. "I think we've been here before . . . on our first adventure with the silver whistle."

2   "I think you're right, Inch."

3   "Weird," said Lily. "It's hot here, not fall weather like at school."

What season is it where the friends are?

4   "Well, I don't know how being in a meadow in the middle of a woods is going to help us with our project!" Pepper said. "Blow that whistle again and get us out of here!"

5   A buzzing sound made the foursome turn around.

What do you think the buzzing sound is?

6   A bee hovered above them.

7   "Betty!" Inch and Miles said.

8   "Hey," the bee said. "You two again . . . and you brought friends this time. I suppose you came for honey."

What is the bee's name?

9   "Actually," Miles said, "we have a problem and we're looking for help. We need to do a project for Open House at our school. We all want to do different things."

GO ON

Heroes of Beesville *continued*

10   "Sorry guys, we bees make honey, so we can't help you," Betty said.

11   "Told you!" Pepper said to Miles. "Blow that whistle again and get us back home!"

12   Miles blew the silver whistle. When they opened their eyes, they stood in exactly the same spot—a field of clover.

> **Why do you think the whistle didn't work?**

13   "Maybe you didn't blow hard enough," Inch told Miles. "Try again."

14   The four classmates huddled together. Then Miles blew the whistle with all the breath he could muster.

> **Do you think the whistle will work this time?**

15   When they opened their eyes again, they were in the same spot.

16   Miles blew the whistle three more times and exactly the same thing happened.

17   "Does that mean we're stuck here?" Inch asked.

18   "As long as we're here, we could help Betty and the bees," Lily said.

19   "Lily's right," Miles said. "Betty, how can we help?"

20   "Well, I'm not sure you can. We bees have a problem—a life-and-death problem."

21   "Wow!" said Inch. "That sounds bad. What is it?"

22   "Ima Skunk," Betty said.

23   Inch, Miles, Lily, and even Pepper giggled.

Why do the four friends laugh?

24   "You don't look like a skunk. You look like a bee," said Pepper with a smile.

25   Betty looked confused. Then she laughed too. "No, no. Ima is a skunk, a real one . . . and a thief! Twice this summer she has found our **hive** and taken our honey. If she steals again, we won't have enough honey for winter. The colony will be done for."

What is the bees' life-and-death problem?

26   "But we don't know how to make honey," Lily said.

27   "So what do you know how to do?" Betty asked. "Everyone's good at something!"

28   "I'm pretty good at drawing," Miles said.

29   a"I know a lot about animals and bugs," said Inch.

30   "I'm good at building things," said Pepper.

31   "I'm good at acting, singing, and dancing," said Lily, doing a little dance.

32   Betty buzzed in circles over the clover. "Do you think you could use any of those talents to help us with Ima Skunk?"

Make Sense of Words When you come to a word you don't know, you can try to understand the meaning by:

- using picture clues.

- rereading the sentence and using the *context clues*. These are the other words in the sentence and the paragraph.

- breaking the word into parts. Sometimes you will find one or more words you know within a word.

- using the dictionary or asking an adult.

Think about the word **hive** in paragraph 25. Reread the context clues in paragraph 25.

1. a. What animal uses a **hive**?

   _____

   b. What is stored in a **hive**?

   _____

   c. What is a **hive**?

   _____

d. Draw a picture of a **hive**.

Read with Understanding   The animal that is going to help the friends learn about cooperation is a bee. What would have been another good prediction? What other animal could teach Inch, Miles, Lily, and Pepper about cooperation?

Ⓐ a snake

Ⓑ a cow

Ⓒ an ant

Ⓓ a frog

Inch, Miles, Lily, and Pepper are each good at different things. Draw a picture of each of the friends doing whatever they are good at.

Inch

Miles

Lily

Pepper

Write to Learn How do you think Inch, Miles, Lily, and Pepper will help Betty and the bees? Will they all cooperate and use their special talents? Write out what you think the friends' plan will be to save the honey from Ima Skunk.

_____

_____

_____

_____

_____

_____

_____

_____

_____

_____

_____

Lesson 9

from **The Grandma Mix-Up**

• *Chapter Book Excerpt*

Heads Up This story is part of a chapter book called *The Grandma Mix-Up*. You will read about Pip and his two grandmas. The people (or animals) in a story are called the *characters*. As you read, think about the characters. Authors can tell you what characters look like or think. You can learn about characters by what they say or how they act. Think of yourself as a character. On the next page you will see a stick figure labeled "Me." On the lines, write things about you. Write how you look, what you think, or how you act. Write things you like to do. All of these things describe your *character*.

ME

Good readers think while they read. One way of thinking while you read is to *ask yourself questions*. As you read this story, you will notice Think-Along Questions. Stop and answer these questions. Then read on. You may add questions of your own. Also, as you read, circle or highlight words you don't know.

from **The Grandma Mix-Up**
by Emily Arnold McCully

My Thoughts

1   Pip's mom and dad were taking a trip.

2   "We will be gone two days and two nights," said Pip's mom. "Grandma Nan will take care of you."

3   Mom and Dad and Pip went downstairs to wait for Grandma Nan.

4   "Here she comes!" cried Pip. "Hi, Grandma Nan!"

How do you think Pip feels about Grandma Nan?

5   "Hello, hello," said Grandma Nan. "How is my good grandchild?"

6   Just then a taxi raced up. Out popped Grandma Sal. "Here I am," she called.

7   "Did you ask Grandma Sal to baby-sit?" Mom asked Dad.

8   "Did you ask Grandma Nan to baby-sit?" Dad asked Mom.

9   "Now what will we do?"

What is the problem?

10   "No matter," said Grandma Sal. "We can both baby-sit!"

11   "Are you sure?" asked Dad.

12   "Run along," said Grandma Sal. "We will have a fine time."

13   "Good-bye, Pip," said Dad.

GO ON

The Grandma Mix-Up *continued*

14   "We will miss you," said Mom.

15   They hugged Pip good-bye and rode away in a taxi.

16   "Well!" said Grandma Nan. "Let's get busy!"

17   "Let's relax!" said Grandma Sal. "Open your treat bag, Pip."

18   "Gummy bears," said Pip. "Thank you!"

19   "Come upstairs," said Grandma Nan. "First thing in the morning, I inspect your room."

20   Pip followed her upstairs.

21   "Oh, Pip," said Grandma Nan sadly. "Your room is a mess! We must clean it up!"

22   Pip put away the socks and trucks and crayons, and pulled up the bed covers. Grandma Nan was very **strict**!

23   "Pip! Pip!" called Grandma Sal from the backyard. "Come down and show me your bike!"

What is Grandma Sal like?

24   Pip ran outside.

25   "Look at you!" said Grandma Sal. "You are a super-duper rider!"

26   "Hi-ho," called Grandma Nan. "It is noon on the dot. Time to eat lunch."

27   Pip and Grandma Sal went inside.

28   "You may have tuna with sprouts," said Grandma Nan.

29   "Or an apple, some nuts, a marshmallow, cereal, pretzels, or corned-beef hash," said Grandma Sal.

30   It was too hard to choose. "I'm not hungry," Pip said.

What do you think is wrong with Pip?

31   "Oh, dear. I don't like the sound of that," said Grandma Nan. "Maybe a nap is in order."

32   "You bet your life!" said Grandma Sal. She plopped down onto the sofa.

33   "See you later, Pip."

Make Sense of Words When you come to a word you don't know, you can try to understand the meaning by:

- using picture clues.

- rereading the sentence and using the *context clues*. These are the other words in the sentence and the paragraph.

- breaking the word into parts. Sometimes you will find one or more words you know within a word.

- using the dictionary or asking an adult.

1. a. In paragraph 22, Grandma Nan is described as **strict**. Below, write what Grandma Nan does at Pip's house. What are her actions?

Grandma Nan's Actions

_____

_____

_____

_____

b. How would you describe Grandma Nan?

I describe Grandma Nan as

_____

_____

_____

_____

c. Now look up **strict** in the dictionary. Write the meaning below.

_____

_____

_____

_____

d. Write an example of someone else (real or made-up) who is **strict**.

_____

_____

_____

_____

Read with Understanding You have read about Grandma Nan and Grandma Sal. You know about their characters. Choose which action Grandma Sal would likely do later in the story.

Ⓐ make Pip take a bath

Ⓑ let Pip eat pizza and watch television

Ⓒ tell Pip to practice his addition facts

Ⓓ send Pip to bed on time

Understand by Seeing It Grandma Nan and
Grandma Sal are very different. To show how things are
alike and different, you can use a Venn diagram. Read
the statements below. Put the letter of each statement
in the correct space in the diagram. To do this, decide
who the statement describes—Grandma Nan, Grandma
Sal, or both grandmas.

Grandma Nan   **Both**   **Grandma Sal**

A. wants to keep things neat

B. likes to take naps

C. likes everything to be on time

D. thinks kids should eat whatever they want

E. loves Pip

F. thinks kids should eat healthy food

G. likes to have fun

Dear Mom and Dad,

_____

_____

_____

_____

_____

_____

_____

_____

Love, Pip

Lesson 10

from Sagebrush

• *Historical Fiction*

Heads Up   You will be reading a story about an Indian boy named Little Eagle. He finds a buffalo calf. He decides to take care of it. Indians were supposed to hunt buffalo, not keep them as pets. Little Eagle doesn't care. He promises to keep his calf alive.

What do you think Little Eagle will be like? What words do you think will describe his character? Write them in the box below.

Little Eagle

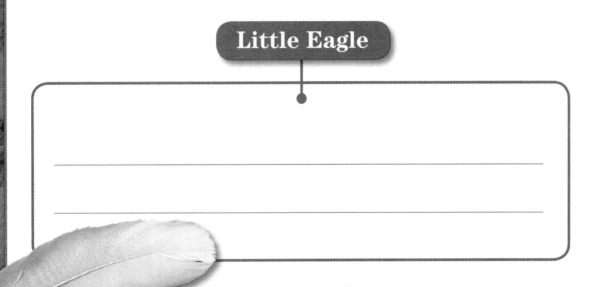

from *Sagebrush*
by Bonnie Highsmith Taylor

1   Suddenly Little Eagle woke up. He heard a sound behind him.

2   He jumped to his feet. Little Eagle looked all around.

3   The sound came again. It was a sound he had never heard before.

4   Little Eagle put an arrow in his bow. He crept slowly toward the **sagebrush**. He crept toward the sound.

Why does Little Eagle put an arrow in his bow?

5   He stood very still. His heart beat fast.

6   The sound came once more. It was louder this time.

7   "It sounds like a baby," thought Little Eagle. "A hungry baby. Crying for food."

8   Little Eagle dropped his bow and arrow. He moved closer to the sagebrush. He knelt on the ground and parted the branches.

9   A little buffalo calf lay in the sagebrush. Its wide eyes stared at the boy.

10   Little Eagle smiled. He slowly reached out his hand.

11   The animal cried softly. It looked afraid.

What do you think happened to the buffalo calf?

12   Little Eagle spoke gently. "Poor little one," he said. "What happened to your mother? Did the hunters kill her? Are you all alone? Are you hungry?"

13   The little buffalo's ears stood up. It listened to the Indian boy's words.

14   Then it licked Little Eagle's hand. It made a loud sucking noise.

15   "Ah! You are hungry, little one," said Little Eagle. "But there is no food in my hand."

16   He bent over the young animal. He wrapped his arms around its neck. He put his face in its soft fur.

17   "I will take you home with me," the Indian boy said. "I will feed you. And I will take care of you. You will be my very own. And I will call you Sagebrush. Because that's where I found you."

What will the other Indians think?

18   Little Eagle returned to the camp. It was late in the day. He had Sagebrush with him.

19   The other Indians watched Little Eagle and the buffalo. What a sight they made! How the Indians laughed!

GO ON ⇨

Sagebrush *continued*

20   Little Eagle struggled with the young buffalo. First he would push from behind. Then he would pull from the front. Then the calf would run a few steps. Little Eagle would hurry to catch up.

21   "Ah!" shouted a young brave. "The mighty hunter has returned. Look! He has captured a great bull. All by himself."

22   "Yes," cried another. "Tonight we shall have a big feast. And there will be meat to eat all winter."

23   The women and children laughed too.

24   Little Eagle walked on. He held his head high. He tried to look proud.

25   Little Eagle's father came toward him. Gray Hawk did not look pleased.

26   "My son," he said. "What is the meaning of this?"

27   "The calf was left all alone," Little Eagle explained. "Its mother must have been killed. The calf would have starved to death."

28   Little Eagle patted the calf's head. "I will take care of it," he said. "It will be my very own. I have named the calf Sagebrush."

29   "You should have killed it out there," Gray Hawk said. "For it will die anyway."

30   "No! No!" the boy cried.

31   Little Eagle fell to his knees. He hugged Sagebrush close to him. "Sagebrush will not die! I will take good care of the calf."

32   "An Indian has no time for such foolishness," Gray Hawk said. "And how will you feed such a young animal? It must have milk from its mother."

33   "Sagebrush will live!" Little Eagle insisted. "You will see! Sagebrush *will* live!"

How do you think Little Eagle will feed Sagebrush?

Make Sense of Words   When you come to a word you don't know, you can try to understand the meaning by:

- using picture clues.

- rereading the sentence and using the *context clues*. These are the other words in the sentence and the paragraph.

- breaking the word into parts. Sometimes you will find one or more words you know within a word.

- using the dictionary or asking an adult.

1. a. Why does Little Eagle name the buffalo calf **Sagebrush?**

_____

_____

_____

   b. The word **sagebrush** can be broken up into two words. Write the words below.

_____   _____

   c. The word *brush* has many meanings. Look it up in the dictionary. Write the meaning that best fits with this story.

_____

_____

d. Now look up the word *sage*. Write the meaning below.

_____

_____

e. Think about the meanings of the word parts. Think about how **sagebrush** was used in the story. What do you think **sagebrush** means?

_____

_____

f. In the box below, draw a picture of Sagebrush in the **sagebrush**.

Read with Understanding In this story, you learn what Little Eagle is like. Which sentence describes him?

Ⓐ Little Eagle is caring.

Ⓑ Little Eagle is mean.

Ⓒ Little Eagle only cares about himself.

Ⓓ Little Eagle always obeys his father.

Understand by Seeing It You learn a lot about Little Eagle in this story. Think of some words that describe Little Eagle. Write them in the chart below. Then tell why that word fits Little Eagle. Use events from the story.

Little Eagle is . . .	Because . . .

Write to Learn   You now know about Little Eagle's character. Write what you think will happen to Little Eagle and Sagebrush.

_____

_____

_____

_____

_____

_____

_____

_____

_____

_____

Lesson 11

Night Senses

from Your Big Backyard

• *Magazine Article*

Heads Up   Read through the magazine article to match the animals with their super sense. You will be rereading the article. Wait until the second reading to answer the Think-Along Questions.

Draw a line from the animals to their super senses.

Moths	Hearing
Cats	Sight
Owls	Touch
Foxes	Smell
Raccoons	
Bats	

Now reread the article. Good readers think while they read. One way of thinking while you read is to *ask yourself questions*. As you read this article, you will notice Think-Along Questions. Stop and answer these questions. Then read on. You may add questions of your own. Also, as you read, circle or highlight words you don't know.

Night Senses
from *Your Big Backyard* **magazine**

1   Lots of creatures are busy at night. When other animals sleep, they hunt for food and mates. To do these things in the dark, the animals must see, hear, smell, or touch very well. That is why . . .

2   Night Animals Have Super Senses.

What are the five senses?

Sight

3   There is very little light at night. But owls have eyes that can catch more light than your eyes can. So owls see better in the dark.

Why do owls need to see in the dark?

GO ON

Night Senses *continued*

Hearing

4   Foxes have very large, pointed ears that can catch sounds well. Foxes can also move their ears around. That helps tell them where the sounds are coming from.

Why do foxes need to hear well in the dark?

5   Bats make very high sounds. The sounds bounce off nearby objects and come back to their ears as **echoes**. The echoes tell bats where the objects are.

Smell

6   When female moths are ready to mate, they send out a special scent. Males pick up the scent with their feelers.

Touch

7   Raccoons don't need to see to catch their food. They dip their hands in streams and feel for tasty frogs and fish.

8   Cats use whiskers to feel their way in the dark. Whiskers can feel things, just as fingers can.

Make Sense of Words When you come to a word you don't know, you can try to understand the meaning by:

- using picture clues.

- rereading the sentence and using the *context clues*. These are the other words in the sentence and the paragraph.

- breaking the word into parts. Sometimes you will find one or more words you know within a word.

- using the dictionary or asking an adult.

Paragraph 5 talks about **echoes**.

1. a. What do you think an **echo** is? Write your prediction below.

_____

_____

   b. Now look up **echo** in the dictionary. Write the definition below.

_____

_____

c. Where could you hear an **echo**?

_____

_____

d. Draw a picture of an **echo** in the box below.

What special sense do moths have?

Ⓐ Moths use whiskers to feel their way in the dark.

Ⓑ Moths have eyes that can catch more light than human eyes can.

Ⓒ Moths make very high sounds that bounce off objects and come back as echoes.

Ⓓ Female moths send out a special scent that males can pick up with their feelers.

Reread the story. As you read, fill in the chart below. The chart will show the special senses of all of the animals.

Night Animal	Special Sense	How the Sense Helps the Animal at Night

Write to Learn   Choose one of the animals from the story. Write your own story about that animal. In the story, have the animal use its special sense at night.

Lesson 12

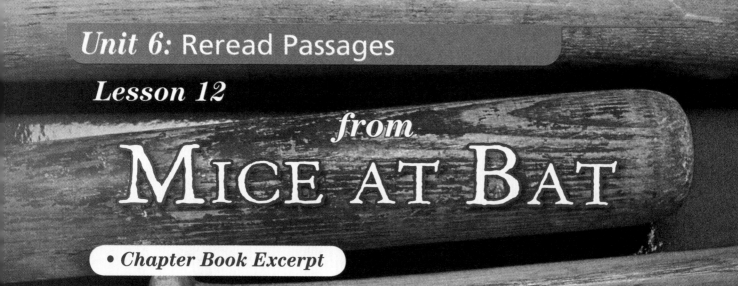

from
MICE AT BAT

- *Chapter Book Excerpt*

Heads Up Sometimes reading something once is not enough. You may have to reread to get all the facts. This will help you understand what you read.

Look quickly through the story *Mice at Bat*. This story is about a group of mice that forms a baseball team. Find ten words that you think will be important in the story. Write them below. Then read the story again.

My Key Words

_____ _____

_____ _____

_____ _____

_____ _____

from Mice at Bat
by Kelly Oechsli

My Thoughts

1   At midnight Kevin took the roll call. All the Mighty Mites were there.

2   The air was cool. The moon was full and bright. It was a great night for a ball game.

3   The Mighty Mites ran onto the **field**.

4   "Hurray!" shouted the fans.

5   The Boomers ran onto the field.

6   "HURRAY!" shouted the fans.

Who do most of the fans want to win the game?

7   Old Casey met with the two **captains**. "Everybody plays," he said. "And nobody argues."

8   "Shake," said Kevin.

9   "Shake," said Artie.

10   "PLAY BALL!" called Old Casey.

11   Young Willie stepped up to the plate. The Boomers' pitcher wound up. He threw the first pitch—*CRACK!*

12   Willie hit the ball. It flew over the second baseman's head.

13   Lou was up next—*CRACK!*

14   The ball flew over the fence.

15   When their turn at bat ended, the Mighty Mites had three runs.

16   Then the Boomers came to bat.

17   *CRACK! CRACK! CRACK! CRACK!*

GO ON

My Thoughts

18   They scored four runs.

19   The fans went wild.

20   "This is some game," said one fan.

21   "This is the game of the year!" cried another.

22   In the second inning, the Mites played better. Young Willie threw the ball. José caught it.

23   "Out! Out!" shouted Old Casey.

24   Each inning the Netter caught everything in sight. But the Boomers stayed ahead 4 to 3.

25   In the seventh inning the Mighty Mites took the lead. They scored five runs.

26   Then the Boomers were up.

How do you think the Boomers will do this inning?

27   *CRACK! CRACK! CRACK!*

28   They loaded the bases.

29   "TIME OUT!" called Artie. "I am calling in Big Jax."

30   "Who is Big Jax?" asked Kevin.

31   Artie smiled. "He is our pinch hitter."

32   Big Jax marched to the plate.

33   The Mites ran to the umpire. "He is not one of us!" the Mites yelled.

34   "But he is one of us," said Artie. "He is wearing our uniform."

35   "I smell a rat," muttered Young Willie.

36   Old Casey looked in the rule book. Then he shook his head. "RAT . . . er . . . BATTER UP!" he called.

What kind of animal is Big Jax?

37   Big Jax waved the bat high over his head. "Watch out, mister pitcher," he called. "If you throw that ball near the plate, I will blast it to the moon."

38   Rusty pitched a fastball right over the plate.

39   *CRACK–K–K!*

40   Big Jax was not kidding. He hit that ball right out of the park.

41   The score was tied.

Make Sense of Words When you come to a word you don't know, you can try to understand the meaning by:

- using picture clues.

- rereading the sentence and using the *context clues*. These are the other words in the sentence and the paragraph.

- breaking the word into parts. Sometimes you will find one or more words you know within a word.

- using the dictionary or asking an adult.

Some words have more than one meaning. To figure out the right meaning, see what makes sense in the story.

1. Paragraph 3 includes the word **field**. Reread the sentence. Now read the meanings below. Which meaning best fits **field** in this story?

   Ⓐ an area used to grow crops

   Ⓑ a subject that a person is an expert in

   Ⓒ an area where a battle is fought

   Ⓓ a playing area for a sport

2. Paragraph 7 includes the word **captains**. Reread the sentence. Now read the meanings below. Which meaning best fits **captain** in this story?

Ⓐ a person in charge of a ship

Ⓑ the police officer who is in charge

Ⓒ a leader of a sport's team

Ⓓ a person in charge of a spacecraft

Read with Understanding Reread the story. Then put the following events in the right order.

_____ Big Jax hit the ball out of the park.

_____ The Mighty Mites scored five runs in one inning.

_____ Old Casey yelled, "PLAY BALL!"

_____ Lou hit the ball over the fence.

Understand by Seeing It Rereading a story will help you remember details. Read through *Mice at Bat* again. Then write events from the story. Put them in the right order.

Baseball Dreams

• *Short Story*

Heads Up Do you have a sport that you love to play? Write about it below.

_____

_____

_____

_____

As you read, use what you learned in the lessons. Make predictions while you read. Think about what the characters are like. Reread passages to recall facts and details. Answer the Think-Along Questions as you read.

Baseball Dreams

Lyle loved baseball more than anything else. He played baseball after school each day. He played baseball every weekend. He thought about baseball all the time. He even dreamed about baseball.

What is something you love to do?

Last Monday, a new boy came to school. He was put in Lyle's class. When he came into the room, Miss Ramirez introduced him.

"Everyone, listen carefully. This is Jiro Ito. He is a new student in our class. Jiro's family comes from Japan. Jiro, say hello to everyone."

"Hello, everyone. Nice to meet you all." Jiro looked down at his shoes. He didn't say another word. Even so, everyone was surprised that Jiro spoke English as well as they did.

At lunch, Lyle introduced himself to Jiro. He wanted to ask Jiro something.

"Do people play baseball in Japan?" asked Lyle.

Why does Jiro look down at his shoes when talking to the class?

Jiro answered, "Yes. Baseball is very popular where I come from."

Then the bell rang. All the children formed a line and went back to their classrooms.

The next day at lunch, Jiro talked to Lyle. "I saw you playing baseball with your friends yesterday. Do you think I could play on your team?"

"I'm not sure," said Lyle. "Meet us for practice today in the park. We can ask the coach what he thinks."

What do you think the coach will say?

Later that afternoon, Lyle's team practiced in the park. When Jiro showed up, Lyle introduced him to the coach.

"Grab a bat, Jiro," said Coach. "Let's see what you can do."

Jiro walked to the plate. He held the bat just right, but he didn't look up.

Lyle was worried. He thought to himself, "How can he hit the ball if he doesn't look at it?"

GO ON

Baseball Dreams *continued*

Just then, the pitcher threw the ball. Jiro looked up as the ball flew toward him. Jiro hit the ball on his first try. Everyone heard a loud crack like thunder. The ball whizzed past the outfielders. Then it sailed over the fence. Jiro hit the next ball just as hard, and the next one too.

How do you think Jiro feels when he hits the balls over the fence?

Lyle ran to Jiro. "You're a great hitter!"

"Thank you," Jiro said. "I love baseball. It's my favorite sport. I even dream about it sometimes."

1. Which prediction is most likely to come true?

    Ⓐ Jiro will become a regular player on Lyle's baseball team.

    Ⓑ Lyle will quit the baseball team.

    Ⓒ Lyle will tell Jiro they can't be friends.

    Ⓓ The coach will make Jiro leave the baseball field.

2. Which word best describes Lyle?

    Ⓐ angry

    Ⓑ friendly

    Ⓒ careless

    Ⓓ rude

3. What country is Jiro from? Reread the story if you need to.

    Ⓐ China

    Ⓑ Canada

    Ⓒ India

    Ⓓ Japan

Understand by Seeing It
Think about the characters of Lyle and Jiro. What are they like? Write two words to describe each below. Then find facts from the story to back up your descriptions.

Lyle is . . .	Because . . .

Jiro is . . .	Because . . .

Write to Learn Jiro was thankful to continue playing baseball after he moved. Imagine that you moved to Japan. What would you miss most if you could no longer do it?

Your Life in Japan

_____

_____

_____

_____

_____

_____

_____

_____

_____

_____

The City Mouse and the Country Mouse

• *Aesop's Fable*

Listening comprehension is a valuable skill. Learning and practicing good listening skills will be helpful to you in your life inside and outside of school. When you listen, it is important to focus your attention on the speaker.

Listen as your teacher reads the fable "The City Mouse and the Country Mouse." Then answer the questions below.

1. What is one food the Country Mouse served the City Mouse when he visited?

_____